CW00419906

Contents

*G = gold; P = platinum; ( ) = the line must be played but cannot be assessed for a Medal.

Doin' Polly's Thing!

Trad. arr. James Rae

© 2004 by The Associated Board of the Royal Schools of Music

AB 3024

Song of the Southern Pacific Nightbirds

Paul Harris

© 2004 by The Associated Board of the Royal Schools of Music

AB 3024

Sonatina in G

G. Benda arr. Sally Adams

© 2004 by The Associated Board of the Royal Schools of Music

AB 3024

Moonwalk Blues

Paul Harris

© 2004 by The Associated Board of the Royal Schools of Music

AB 3024

The Irish Washing-Machine

Trad. arr. Mark Goddard

© 2004 by The Associated Board of the Royal Schools of Music

AB 3024

Invention No. 1 in C

from *Inventions and Sinfonias*, BWV 772

J. S. **Bach** arr. Paul Harris

© 2004 by The Associated Board of the Royal Schools of Music

AB 3024

Deadline

Robert Tucker

© 2004 by The Associated Board of the Royal Schools of Music

AB 3024

Theme and Variation

First movement from Sonatina in C

Vanhal arr. Sally Adams

© 2004 by The Associated Board of the Royal Schools of Music

AB 3024

Coda

Braid the Raven Hair

from *The Mikado*

Sullivan arr. Gordon Lewin

© 2004 by The Associated Board of the Royal Schools of Music

AB 3024

Goldfinch

Robert Tucker

© 2004 by The Associated Board of the Royal Schools of Music

AB 3024

Riverside Stroll

Gordon Lewin

© 2004 by The Associated Board of the Royal Schools of Music

AB 3024

21

The Poor Orphan Child

from *Album for the Young*, Op. 68

Schumann arr. Gordon Lewin

© 2004 by The Associated Board of the Royal Schools of Music

AB 3024

The Curtain Drawn

G. Farnaby arr. Gordon Lewin

© 2004 by The Associated Board of the Royal Schools of Music

AB 3024

Vegas Vacation

James Rae

© 2004 by The Associated Board of the Royal Schools of Music

AB 3024

Dance of the Circles

Paul Harris

© 2004 by The Associated Board of the Royal Schools of Music

AB 3024

dedicated to Sir Malcolm Arnold

Fit for Flutes

Robert Tucker

© 2004 by The Associated Board of the Royal Schools of Music